MW00696109

This Is Me

A MINDFUL, AUTOBIOGRAPHICAL JOURNAL

Explore and celebrate the uniqueness that makes you who you are.

This Is Me allows you to connect with your emotions on a wonderful journey of exploration and discovery.

From traditions you'd like to pass on, people you can't live without, to books that kept you up all night, create a trove of handwritten delights and insights to be treasured.

NAME:

....

ADDRESS:

....

....

....

....

PHONE NUMBER:

....

EMAIL:

....

Who
I Am

Facts and figures all about me

Parents and grandparents
& how I'm like them

....

....

....

....

....

....

....

....

....

....

....

....

....

....

....

....

....

Life events that have shaped me

....

....

....

....

....

....

....

....

....

....

....

....

....

....

....

....

....

Important life lessons I have learned

Adolescent moments I'd like to forget

....

....

....

....

....

....

....

....

....

....

....

....

....

....

....

....

....

....

A letter to my younger self

Things that keep me awake at night

....
....
....
....
....
....
....
....
....
....
....
....
....
....
....
....
....
....

Dates that should always be remembered

....
....
....
....
....
....
....
....
....
....
....
....
....
....
....
....
....
....
....
....
....

What's most important to me

Shade in the wheel according to how important each life segment is to you. The more you shade the more important it is to you.

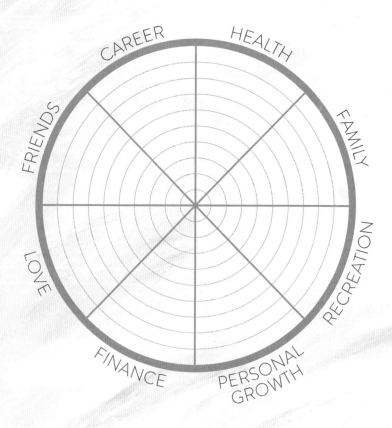

Values I live by

My greatest strengths

....

....

....

....

....

....

My greatest weaknesses

....

....

....

....

....

....

Childhood memories I appreciate

....
....
....
....
....
....
....
....
....
....
....
....
....
....
....
....

The type of friend I believe I am

....
....
....
....
....
....
....
....
....
....
....
....
....
....
....
....
....

How I want to celebrate
my next birthday

Friends & Family

Family relationships I relish

....
....
....
....
....
....
....
....
....
....
....
....
....
....
....
....
....
....
....

*Parental techniques used by my
parents that I think were great*

....
....
....
....
....
....

*Parental techniques used by my
parents that I would never use*

....
....
....
....
....
....

The Family Member ...

I TALK TO THE MOST:

....

....

I LOOK LIKE THE MOST:

....

....

I'M TALLER THAN:

....

....

I WISH I COULD BE FOR A DAY:

....

....

I MOST ADMIRE:

....

....

The Family Member ...

THAT TELLS THE BEST STORIES:

....

....

WHO IS THE FUNNIEST:

....

....

WHO IS BEST IN A CRISIS:

....

....

I SHOULD SEE MORE OFTEN:

....

....

LISTENS REALLY WELL:

....

....

Acquaintances I'd like to
get to know better

....
....
....
....
....
....
....
....
....
....
....
....
....
....
....
....
....
....
....

Friendships I cherish

The Friend Who ...

IS MOST LIKE ME:

....

....

IS MOST DIFFERENT TO ME:

....

....

I'LL BE FRIENDS WITH FOREVER:

....

....

I WISH I COULD BE FOR A DAY:

....

....

I MOST ADMIRE:

....

....

The Friend Who ...

TELLS THE BEST STORIES:

....

....

IS THE FUNNIEST:

....

....

IS BEST IN A CRISIS:

....

....

I SHOULD SEE MORE OFTEN:

....

....

LISTENS REALLY WELL:

....

....

Romantic moments to never forget

....
....
....
....
....
....
....
....
....
....
....
....
....
....
....
....
....
....

Love lessons I've learnt

....
....
....
....
....
....
....
....
....
....
....
....
....
....
....
....
....
....

Relationships

FIRST KISS:

....

....

FIRST CRUSH:

....

....

BEST DATE EVER:

....

....

HEARTBREAKS I'VE HAD OR CAUSED:

....

....

CRINGY MOMENTS I'D RATHER FORGET:

....

....

Relationships

THE ONE I'M GLAD GOT AWAY:

....

....

MY ONLINE DATING TAGLINE:

....

....

MOST ROMANTIC GESTURE:

....

....

PERFECT PARTNER CRITERIA:

....

....

....

....

....

Favorite traits in others

....
....
....
....
....
....

Least favorite traits in others

....
....
....
....
....
....

People I've loved and lost

....
....
....
....
....
....
....
....
....
....
....
....
....
....
....
....
....
....
....
....
....

Education & Work

Schools & colleges I went to

....

....

....

....

....

....

....

....

....

....

....

....

....

....

....

....

....

....

....

....

People who I admire or who have inspired me

....

....

....

....

....

....

....

....

....

....

....

....

....

....

....

....

....

....

School memories that make me smile

School memories I wish I could forget

....

....

....

....

....

....

....

....

....

....

....

....

....

....

....

....

....

School friends I remember
for the good times

....
....
....
....
....
....
....
....
....
....
....
....
....
....
....
....
....

Subjects I loved

Subjects I loathed

....
....
....
....
....
....
....
....
....
....
....
....
....
....
....
....
....
....

Subjects I would like to study now

Things I did well during my education

....
....
....
....
....
....
....
....
....
....
....
....
....
....
....
....
....
....

Things I could have done better,
if only I had tried

....

....

....

....

....

....

....

....

....

....

....

....

....

....

....

....

....

....

What I wanted to do when I grew up

What I actually do now

....
....
....
....
....
....
....
....
....
....
....
....
....
....
....
....

Steps I took to get to where I am today

*People I work with that make
the day worthwhile*

....

....

....

....

....

....

....

....

....

....

....

....

....

....

....

....

....

....

My dream job and the skills I need

....

....

....

....

....

....

....

....

....

....

....

....

....

....

....

....

....

....

....

My ambitions for my retirement

....
....
....
....
....
....
....
....
....
....
....
....
....
....
....
....
....
....
....

Sections
of Four

Pastimes and passions to start

1

2

3

4

Bad habits to ditch

1

2

3

4

Things I've completed

1

2

3

4

Inspirational ideas that could bring success

1

2

3

4

My guilty pleasures

1

2

3

4

Memory evoking smells

1

2

3

4

Words to describe me

1

2

3

4

Fears & phobias

1

2

3

4

Resolutions I've broken

1

2

3

4

Promises I've made

1

2

3

4

Favorite board games

1

2

3

4

Best views

1

2

3

4

Most loved sounds

1

2

3

4

What makes me different

1

2

3

4

Fashion, Films & Fixtures

*Movies I enjoyed so much, I ate
all the popcorn without noticing*

....
....
....
....
....
....
....
....
....
....
....
....
....
....
....
....
....

If my life was a movie,
the title would be

....

....

The person to play me would be

....

....

The plot would be

....

....

....

....

....

Actors I'd love to play opposite

....
....
....
....
....
....

Stars who went out too soon

....
....
....
....
....
....

Movies I wish I had never watched

Television shows I wish I'd written

....
....
....
....
....
....

Television shows that I wish had never ended

....
....
....
....
....
....

Fashions that never should have happened

....
....
....
....
....
....
....
....
....
....
....
....
....
....
....
....
....
....

Labels I wear

....

....

....

....

....

....

Labels I wish I could wear

....

....

....

....

....

....

Belongings of mine I should really donate

....
....
....
....
....
....
....
....
....
....
....
....
....
....
....
....
....
....
....
....
....

Sports and games I love

....
....
....
....
....
....

Sports and games I loathe

....
....
....
....
....
....

Fixtures /sports events I'll never forget

The gadgets I couldn't live without

....
....
....
....
....
....

The gadgets I don't understand

....
....
....
....
....
....

*Imaginary gadgets that
I would invent if I could*

....
....
....
....
....
....
....
....
....
....
....
....
....
....
....
....
....

Books,
Art &
Music

Books that kept me up all night

Books that made me cry

....
....
....
....
....
....

Books that made me laugh

....
....
....
....
....
....

*Books or writers I need to read
(ask others for recommendations)*

....
....
....
....
....
....
....
....
....
....
....
....
....
....
....
....
....

This Or That . . .

eBOOKS	☒	☒	PAPER BOOKS
BOOKMARKS	☒	☒	FOLDING CORNERS
BUY	☒	☒	BORROW
READ ONCE	☒	☒	READ AGAIN
FACT	☒	☒	FICTION
ROMANCE	☒	☒	COMEDY
HARDBACK	☒	☒	PAPERBACK
BOOKSHOP	☒	☒	ONLINE
WRITE IN	☒	☒	KEEP CLEAN

Favorite authors from my youth

....
....
....
....
....
....

Favorite authors right now

....
....
....
....
....
....

Artists I admire

....
....
....
....
....
....

Artists I don't get

....
....
....
....
....
....

Paintings I wish I owned

....
....
....
....
....
....
....
....
....
....
....
....
....
....
....
....
....

The genres of music I love

Music that makes me stick
fingers in my ears

This Or That . . .

CD	☒	☒	DOWNLOAD
SPEAKERS	☒	☒	HEADPHONES
LIVE MUSIC	☒	☒	RECORDED MUSIC
CLASSICAL	☒	☒	HARD ROCK
COUNTRY	☒	☒	PUNK
LIVE RADIO	☒	☒	PLAYLISTS
DANCING	☒	☒	STANDING
LOUD MUSIC	☒	☒	QUIET MUSIC
SING ALONG	☒	☒	LISTEN

Favorite music from my childhood

....
....
....
....
....
....
....
....
....
....
....
....
....
....
....
....
....
....

Favorite music as a teen

....
....
....
....
....
....
....
....
....
....
....
....
....
....
....
....
....

Songs that remind me of the good times

....
....
....
....
....
....
....
....
....
....
....
....
....
....
....
....
....

Tracks to take everywhere

....
....
....
....
....
....
....
....
....
....
....
....
....
....
....
....
....
....
....

Songs I sing out loud

....

....

....

....

....

....

....

....

....

....

....

....

....

....

....

Instruments I play

....

....

....

....

....

....

Instruments I wish I could play

....

....

....

....

....

....

Food & Parties

This Or That . . .

ICE CREAM	☒	☒	SORBET
DARK CHOCOLATE	☒	☒	MILK CHOCOLATE
SWEET	☒	☒	SAVOURY
DARK TOAST	☒	☒	LIGHT TOAST
COFFEE	☒	☒	TEA
RESTAURANT	☒	☒	HOME COOKED
MEAT	☒	☒	VEG
WINE	☒	☒	WATER
TOMATO KETCHUP	☒	☒	MAPLE SYRUP

Favorite sweet treats

....
....
....
....
....
....
....
....
....
....
....
....
....
....
....
....
....
....
....
....

Historical figures I would invite for tea

....

....

....

....

....

....

....

....

....

....

....

....

....

....

....

....

*If I had one meal left on
Earth, it would be*

....
....
....
....
....
....
....
....
....
....
....
....
....
....
....
....
....

Beverages of choice

....
....
....
....
....
....
....
....
....
....
....
....
....
....
....
....

Top restaurants worth a visit

....
....
....
....
....
....
....
....
....
....
....
....
....
....
....
....
....
....
....
....

Food I like

....
....
....
....
....
....

Food I loathe

....
....
....
....
....
....

Parties worth a mention

Holiday celebrations I'd like to relive

Best gifts ever received

....
....
....
....
....
....

Worst gifts ever received

....
....
....
....
....
....

Spontaneous events I didn't see coming

....
....
....
....
....
....
....
....
....
....
....
....
....
....
....
....
....
....
....
....

My specialty meals:
appetizer, main and dessert

....
....
....
....
....
....
....
....
....
....
....
....
....
....
....
....

Home
&Away

My home and
what I like about it

....

....

....

....

....

....

....

....

....

....

....

....

....

....

....

....

....

Dream home plans

....
....
....
....
....
....
....
....
....
....
....
....
....
....
....
....
....
....

What I'd grab if my house was on fire

....
....
....
....
....
....
....
....
....
....
....
....
....
....
....
....
....
....

Neighbors from heaven

....
....
....
....
....
....

Neighbors from hell

....
....
....
....
....
....

Pets and other animals

Best travel memories worthy of note

....
....
....
....
....
....
....
....
....
....
....
....
....
....
....
....

Perfect travel companions

3 places I've discovered and
don't want to share

1
....
....
....
....
....

2
....
....
....
....
....

3
....
....
....
....
....

Places I love visiting

3 road trips I've taken

1

2

3

Dates I'd choose if I could time travel

Fantasy locations I wish I could visit

1 ....
   ....
   ....
   ....
   ....

2 ....
   ....
   ....
   ....
   ....

3 ....
   ....
   ....
   ....
   ....

Lists of
Seven

7 keepsakes I have

1
....
....

2
....
....

3
....
....

4
....
....

5
....
....

6
....
....

7
....
....

7 traditions I'd like to pass on

1 ....
....

2 ....
....

3 ....
....

4 ....
....

5 ....
....

6 ....
....

7 ....
....

7 things I'd like to take if I was trapped on a desert island

1 ....

....

2 ....

....

3 ....

....

4 ....

....

5 ....

....

6 ....

....

7 ....

....

7 people who have made a
positive impact on my life

1
....
....

2
....
....

3
....
....

4
....
....

5
....
....

6
....
....

7
....
....

7 values I appreciate in others

1 ....
....

2 ....
....

3 ....
....

4 ....
....

5 ....
....

6 ....
....

7 ....
....

7 pieces of wisdom given to me

1
....
....

2
....
....

3
....
....

4
....
....

5
....
....

6
....
....

7
....
....

7 things that make me happy

1
....
....

2
....
....

3
....
....

4
....
....

5
....
....

6
....
....

7
....
....

7 people I couldn't live without

1
....
....

2
....
....

3
....
....

4
....
....

5
....
....

6
....
....

7
....
....

7 overwhelming moments I've experienced

1
....
....

2
....
....

3
....
....

4
....
....

5
....
....

6
....
....

7
....
....

7 places that are special to me

1 ....
....

2 ....
....

3 ....
....

4 ....
....

5 ....
....

6 ....
....

7 ....
....

7 things I wish were true

1
....
....

2
....
....

3
....
....

4
....
....

5
....
....

6
....
....

7
....
....

7 things I wish I hadn't lost

1
....
....

2
....
....

3
....
....

4
....
....

5
....
....

6
....
....

7
....
....

7 wishes I want to come true

1 ....
....

2 ....
....

3 ....
....

4 ....
....

5 ....
....

6 ....
....

7 ....
....

7 things I want to be remembered for

1
....
....

2
....
....

3
....
....

4
....
....

5
....
....

6
....
....

7
....
....

This Is Me

A MINDFUL, AUTOBIOGRAPHICAL JOURNAL

The Mindful Collection, first published by **FROM YOU TO ME LTD**, in August 2018.

There are three titles in the collection:
Forward Thinking, This Is Me & Wonderful Days

To personalise journals and books as well as purchase
other products produced by us, please go to

WWW.FROMYOUTOME.COM

FROM YOU TO ME are committed to a sustainable future for our business,
our customers and our planet. This book is printed and bound in China
on sustainably sourced acid-free paper.

All rights reserved. No part of this publication may be reproduced, stored in a
retrieval system, or transmitted in any form or by any means electronic, mechanical,
photocopying, recording, or otherwise, without the prior written permission of the
copyright owner who can be contacted via the publisher at the following address.

FROM YOU TO ME
Studio 100, The Old Leather Factory
Glove Factory Studios, Holt
Wiltshire, BA14 6RJ, UK

Copyright © 2018 **FROM YOU TO ME LTD**
ISBN 978-1-907860-25-6

3 5 7 9 11 13 15 14 12 10 8 6 4 2
This edition October 2022